Insanity S

Discovered

TONY LOPES

RAVETTE PUBLISHING

Licensed by PSL.

This edition first published by Ravette Publishing 2004.

Printed and bound in Malta for
Ravette Publishing Limited
Unit 3, Tristar Centre
Star Road, Partridge Green
West Sussex RH13 8RA

ISBN: 1 84161 227 8

for Mum, thank you

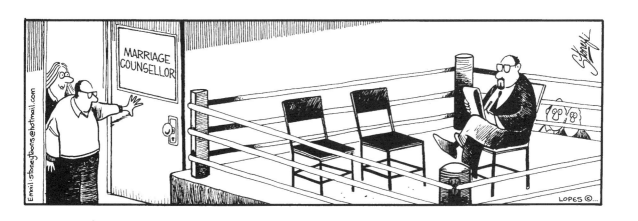

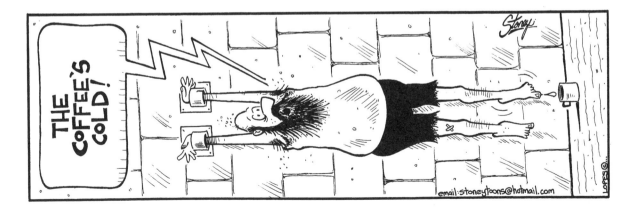